MATHS PLUS
FROM HEINEMANN

C000262291

Interactive
Mental Maths

working with the whole class

5

Peter Patilla

For Year 5 / Primary 6

Heinemann

Heinemann Educational Publishers
Halley Court, Jordan Hill, Oxford, OX2 8EJ
a division of Reed Educational and Professional Publishing Ltd

Heinemann is a registered trademark of Reed Educational and Professional Publishing Ltd

OXFORD   MELBOURNE   AUCKLAND
JOHANNESBURG   BLANTYRE   GABORONE
IBADAN   PORTSMOUTH (NH)   CHICAGO

© Peter Patilla 1999

Heinemann Educational Ltd. All rights reserved. Apart from the duplicating masters, no part of this publication may be reproduced in any material form (including photocopying or storing it in any medium by electronic means and whether or not transiently or incidentally to some other use of this publication) without the prior written permission of the copyright owner, except in accordance with the provisions of the Copyright, Designs and Patents Act 1988 or under the terms of a licence issued by the Copyright Licensing Agency, 90 Tottenham Court Road, London W1P 0LP. Applications for the copyright owner's written permission to reproduce any part of this publication should be addressed in the first instance to the publisher.

The duplicating masters in this book may be photocopied for one-time use as instructional material in a classroom by a teacher, but they may not be copied in unlimited quantities, kept on behalf of others, passed or sold on to third parties, or stored for future use in a retrieval system. If you wish to use the material in any way other than that specified you must apply in writing to the publisher.

First published 1999

03   02   01   00   99
10 9 8 7 6 5 4 3 2 1

ISBN 0 435 02508 2

Designed, typeset and illustrated by AMR
Cover design by Tokay
Cover illustrations by Nick Sharratt
Printed and bound in Great Britain by Athenaeum Press Ltd, Gateshead

Acknowledgements

I wish to thank all the pupils and their teachers who have contributed to the ideas in this book by trialling and working on the activities over the past few years. They have helped develop many of my original thoughts.

My thanks also to teaching and publishing colleagues for their advice, ideas and support.

Many of the activities have been influenced by authors who have written about maths education and how children learn. I am grateful for their research in this area.

Much support was given by Sally Breedon of NES Arnold in producing and providing resources for use in the development of some of the ideas used in this series of books.

Finally, thank you to Thomas and Joseph Shipman, young number enthusiasts, who provided the motivation for collecting all these ideas together.

Peter Patilla

Contents

Introduction

The *Interactive Mental Maths* series is designed to support the implementation of the National Numeracy Strategy and *Improving Mathematics Education 5–14*. Each book contains activities suitable for regular 10-minute sessions with the whole class before the main teaching activity. The mental mathematics skills develop from book to book, often using the same techniques to build up familiarity, comfort and the all-important practice. Timetable 'menus' are provided to assist planning.

Interactive Mental Maths 5 systematically develops three aspects of mental mathematics:

- **Quick recall of facts** Pupils need to develop their maths knowledge in order to quickly recall facts. This includes number facts such as addition and subtraction facts for 20 and 100, and the multiplication and division table facts. It also includes remembering facts, for example, shape names and properties, measurement equivalences, and number properties such as odd and even numbers. Quick recall can also include telling the time.

- **Mental calculations** Pupils need efficient techniques to make mental calculations without resorting to formal taught algorithms or apparatus. Examples include quick additions and subtractions of 9 and 99 as well as finding close differences of large numbers.

- **Mental problem solving** Pupils need to solve word problems, chain calculations, problems involving mental imagery and more complex mental calculations where the operation required may not be immediately obvious. They should learn to solve non-routine problems and know the operations needed to answer them.

Interactive techniques

The suggestions included throughout the book focus upon interactive techniques suitable for direct teaching, usually to a whole class and occasionally to a large group. Lively and appropriate questions, explanations and illustrations are all used to help make mathematics interactive, and ensure that all pupils have the opportunity to explain and illustrate their methods to you and to fellow pupils. Mathematics can also be made participatory by using techniques and strategies to ensure that all pupils take part in the activities to the best of their abilities.

The three teaching devices below will build pupils' confidence and encourage them to take part in whole-class activities.

- **Circle time** Pupils sit in a large circle with you and have full eye contact with each other. This will help them to co-operate more and there will be fewer distractions. Your questioning will be more evenly spread.

- **Show me** Pupils hold up number cards and other simple pieces of apparatus. The format of the activity ensures that everyone takes part. A glance round the responses is a quick and efficient way of assessment. This activity builds up pupils' self-confidence and is an alternative to 'called out' answers. It also gives pupils time to think.

- **Number lines** Active number lines such as number washing lines, counting sticks, and moving a marker along a card strip ensure pupil interaction. They also develop the realization that numbers have positions and intermediate values.

Using the books

Interactive Mental Maths 5 is organized into two-page units, each with a main heading indicating the key skill(s) covered by the activities included. The purpose of the activities, and suggestions for development are shown at the top of the left-hand page.

The activities have been chosen for their high 'repeat value' with a particular year group – in other words, they lend themselves to use on several occasions.

You may choose one or more activities from the same unit for use on different days during a week. Alternatively, you may prefer to vary the activities presented to the children. In this instance the timetable 'menus' on pages 7–9 can be used to assist with planning.

Skills development

By the end of the activities in this book, pupils should have acquired skills in the following areas.

Place value and equivalence

- Knowing place value of any whole number up to one million
- Knowing decimal notations to two places
- Using counting skills to count forward and back in different sized steps
- Multiplying or dividing numbers by 10 or 100
- Estimating, rounding, comparing and ordering numbers
- Using negative numbers
- Knowing equivalences between measurements
- Knowing equivalences of, and between, simple fractions, decimals and percentages

Properties of numbers

- Knowing odd and even numbers
- Recognizing simple counting sequences
- Knowing factors and multiples
- Knowing squares
- Using inverses and commutativity

Calculations

- Knowing by heart addition and subtraction bonds to 20
- Extending knowledge of number bonds to larger numbers
- Quick recall of numbers which total 1, 10 and 100
- Halving and doubling a wide range of numbers
- Calculating with multiples and powers of 10
- Mentally adding and subtracting 2-digit numbers
- Knowing multiplication and division tables facts to 10×10 by heart
- Quick mental addition and subtraction strategies for numbers such as 99
- Using factors and multiples in mental calculations
- Using mental calculations in measurement, money and time contexts

Properties of shapes

- Recognizing and naming most 2D and 3D shapes
- Knowing obvious properties of common 2D and 3D shapes
- Knowing angle properties of common shapes

Development of activities

The following shows the development of different types of participatory activities within the book. Whenever these activities are used, the scope and range can be extended.

Thigh clap

pages: 12, 13, 23, 24, 25, 29
- Counting in 10, 100 and 1000
- Counting forward and back
- Counting in halves
- Quick calculations
- Multiples
- Prime numbers

Number cards

pages: 14, 20, 24, 25, 27, 28, 29, 30
- Number facts to 20
- Number language
- Close differences
- Totalling three 2-digit numbers
- Multiplication and division facts
- Divisibility rules
- Finding remainders
- Mental calculations for multiplication
- Mental calculations for division
- Special numbers
- Factors
- Equivalence of fractions and wholes

Ping pong

pages: 14, 20, 23, 28, 31
- Number pairs to 20
- Doubles and halves
- Adding and subtracting 9 and 99
- Quick addition and subtraction
- Special numbers
- Equivalent fractions

Tell me about

pages: 15, 19, 23, 34, 39
- Number facts to 20
- Position, approximation of numbers
- Position, approximation of measures
- Equivalence, time, measures and money
- Number facts to 100
- Time facts and language

Pass it on

pages: 22, 37
- Quick calculations with powers of 10
- 2D and 3D shapes

Shape totals

pages: 15, 34
- Totalling 3 or more numbers within 20
- Totalling to 100 and to 1

Digital time maker

pages: 39
- Digital time
- 24 hour clock
- Time calculations

Counting stick

pages: 16, 19, 33
- Positions on a number line
- Estimation and rounding
- Estimating decimals

Elastic band strips

pages: 17, 18, 30, 32, 35
- Position of numbers
- Estimation
- Estimation of fractions
- Estimation of tenths
- Estimation of hundredths
- Estimations within 100

Number generator

pages: 17, 18, 20, 21, 26, 31, 35
- Place value
- Number properties
- Rounding
- Calculations with multiples of 10
- Approximating calculations
- Extending multiplication and division
- Calculations with fractions
- Calculating with 100s

Fan numbers

pages: 21, 24, 26, 29, 33, 35
- Calculations with 2-digit numbers
- Multiplication and division facts
- Extending multiplication and division facts
- Number language
- Decimals
- Dividing by 100
- Rounding numbers

Hands up

pages: 16, 22, 26, 28
- Number facts
- Quick calculations
- Multiplication, division and place value
- Odd and even

Decimal place value cards

pages: 32, 33, 35
- Decimals to 2 places
- Ordering decimals
- Decimal facts
- Equivalence and notation of money
- Percentages

Place value grid

pages: 16, 21, 27
- Extended notation
- Counting through multiples of 10, 100 and 1000
- Multiplying and dividing by powers of 10

Show me

pages: 36, 37, 38
- 2D and 3D shapes
- Right angles
- Diagonals
- Positions and directions

Timetable menus

The following tables show one possible activities timetable for the whole year.

Rapid recall of addition and subtraction facts or multiplication and division facts is very important. Daily practice within the mental maths activities is recommended, as pupils need to be comfortable with these facts.

Autumn Term

Week 1		**Week 7**	
Counting patterns		*Number bonds and shapes*	
Thigh clap	*pages 12, 13*	Number cards	*pages 14, 24*
Pendulum count	*page 12*	Fan numbers	*page 24*
Dead stop	*page 13*	Behind the wall	*page 36*
Sound jumps	*page 13*	Show me	*page 36*
Week 2		**Week 8**	
Counting and number facts to 20		*Calculations*	
Pendulum count	*page 12*	Number generator	*page 20*
Sound jumps	*page 13*	Ping pong	*page 20*
Number cards	*page 14*	Number cards	*page 20*
Tell me about	*page 15*	Place value grid	*page 21*
Week 3		**Week 9**	
Number facts to 20		*Calculations and time*	
Number cards	*page 14*	Number generator	*pages 20, 21*
Shape totals	*page 15*	Fan numbers	*page 21*
Ping pong	*page 14*	Digital time maker	*page 39*
Tell me about	*page 15*	Tell me about	*page 39*
Week 4		**Week 10**	
Counting and place value		*Quick calculations*	
Thigh clap	*page 12*	Number cards	*pages 14, 24*
Pendulum count	*page 12*	Cycle cards	*page 22*
Dead stop	*page 13*	Hands up	*page 22*
Place value grid	*page 16*	Tell me about	*page 23*
Counting stick	*page 16*		
		Week 11	
Week 5		*Quick calculations and shape*	
Place value		Cycle cards	*page 22*
Place value grid	*page 16*	Thigh clap	*page 23*
Counting stick	*page 16*	Ping pong	*page 23*
Hands up	*page 16*	Pass it on	*pages 22, 37*
Elastic band strips	*page 17*		
Number generator	*page 17*	**Week 12**	
		Tables	
Week 6		Number cards	*page 24*
Rounding		Thigh clap	*pages 24, 25*
Elastic bands strips	*page 18*	Multiplication square	*page 25*
Number generator	*page 18*		
Counting stick	*page 19*		
Inequality signs	*page 19*		

Spring Term

Week 1		**Week 8**	

Week 1

Counting patterns and multiples

Pendulum count	*page 12*
Thigh clap	*pages 12, 24, 25*

Week 2

Table facts

Number cards	*pages 24, 25*
Fan numbers	*page 24*
Multiplication square	*page 25*

Week 3

Extending table facts

Number generator	*page 26*
Hands up	*page 26*
Fan numbers	*pages 24, 26*
Number cards	*page 27*

Week 4

Place value, estimating and approximating

Place value grid	*pages 16, 27*
Number generator	*pages 17, 18*
Inequality signs	*page 19*
Tell me about	*page 19*

Week 5

Number properties

Number cards	*pages 28, 29*
Hands up	*page 28*
Ping pong	*page 28*
Fan numbers	*page 29*

Week 6

Prime numbers and shape

Thigh clap	*page 29*
Number cards	*page 29*
Fan numbers	*page 29*
I spy	*page 37*

Week 7

Angles and position

Show me	*page 37*
Angle strips	*page 38*
Angle maker	*page 38*
Show me	*page 38*

Week 8

Division, factors and fractions

Number cards	*pages 25, 27, 28, 29*
Number generator	*pages 26, 31*

Week 9

Decimals and time

Decimal place value cards	*page 32*
Elastic band strips	*page 32*
Counting stick	*page 33*
Digital time maker	*page 39*

Week 10

Decimals

Decimal place value cards	*pages 32, 33*
Elastic band strips	*page 32*
Fan numbers	*page 33*
Counting stick	*page 33*

Week 11

Number facts, shape and angles

Guess my number	*page 15*
Number cards	*pages 14, 24, 25, 28, 29*
Show me	*page 37*

Week 12

Hundreds

Tell me about	*page 34*
Shape totals	*page 34*
Number generator	*page 35*
Fan numbers	*page 35*
Elastic band strips	*page 35*

Summer Term

Week 1		Week 7	
Counting skills		**Fractions**	
Thigh clap	*pages 12, 13, 23, 24, 25, 29*	Elastic band strips	*page 30*
		Pendulum count	*page 30*
Counting stick	*pages 16, 19, 33*	Number cards	*page 30*
Pendulum count	*pages 12, 30*	Fraction cards	*page 31*
Sound jumps	*page 13*	Ping pong	*page 31*
Dead stop	*page 13*		

Week 2		Week 8	
Place value and decimals		**Fractions**	
Number generator	*pages 17, 18, 20, 26, 35*	Elastic band strips	*page 30*
		Number generator	*page 31*
Elastic band strips	*pages 17, 18, 32, 35*	Ping pong	*page 31*

Week 9	
Number properties	

Place value grid	*pages 16, 21, 27*	Number cards	*page 28*
Decimal place value cards	*pages 32, 33*	Fan numbers	*page 29*

Week 3		Ping pong	*page 28*
Multiplication		Thigh clap	*page 29*
Number cards	*pages 24, 27*		
Fan numbers	*pages 24, 26*	Week 10	
Number generator	*pages 20, 21, 26*	**Calculations and position**	
Pass it on	*page 22*	Number generator	*pages 20, 21*
		Number cards	*page 20*

Week 4		Fan numbers	*page 21*
Division		Cycle cards	*page 22*
Number generator	*pages 20, 21, 26*	Show me	*page 38*
Number cards	*pages 24, 25, 27*		
Fan numbers	*pages 24, 26*	Week 11	
Hands up	*page 26*	**Number bonds (addition, subtraction, multiplication, division) and time**	

Week 5		Number cards	*pages 14, 24*
Angles and shape		Chain sums	*page 14*
Behind the wall	*page 36*	Tell me about	*pages 15, 39*
Show me	*pages 36, 37*	Digital time maker	*page 39*
Pass it on	*page 37*		
Angle strips	*page 38*	Week 12	
Angle maker	*page 38*	**Percentages and hundreds**	

Week 6		Decimal place value cards	*page 35*
Rounding, equality and estimating		Number generator	*page 35*
Elastic band strips	*page 18*	Fan numbers	*page 35*
Inequality signs	*page 19*	Elastic band strips	*page 35*
Tell me about	*pages 19, 23*		
Counting stick	*page 19*		

As well as trying the suggestions for each term, re-visit other activities for practice, reinforcement and enjoyment.

Resources

To ensure full pupil participation in mental maths activities, a few simple and inexpensive materials are needed. These should be readily available for teacher and pupil use. The materials suggested are used frequently during the activities, and so could form the basis for a mental maths kit. Photocopies are provided for most of these.

Pupil maths kit

Number cards, page 40	Decimal place value cards, page 45
Place value grid, page 41	Angle maker, page 46
Number generator, page 42	Digital time maker, page 47
Fan numbers, page 43	Elastic band strips, see page 11
Fraction cards, page 44	

Teacher resources

Counting stick	Demonstration fan numbers	2D shapes
Maths washing line	Large number cards	3D shapes
Pendulum		

Counting stick

- A counting stick is a length of wood marked off into ten equal sections either with alternate colours or with coloured tape used to make the divisions. The length is arbitrary, although an unnumbered metre stick marked in decimetres is ideal.

- Another possibility is a length of broom handle with marks made with coloured tape.

Pendulum

A counting pendulum can be made by attaching any suitable weight to the end of a long piece of string. The teacher fastens the pendulum so that it swings freely and pupils can count in time with the rhythm of the swing.

Fan numbers

A fan number is simply a set of digits fastened together to make a fan shape. The fans can be used in two ways:

- the set of shown digits are totalled to match a criterion set by the teacher

- the set of digits shown form a 2-digit or 3-digit number.

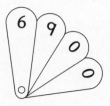

Decimal and non-decimal fans are used. Pupils can either have two fans, one of which is decimal, or they can simply add the decimal point to their fan when it is needed.

Elastic band strips

These are strips of scrap card. An elastic band is threaded on to the card, taut enough not to drop off. The band is moved along the strip to indicate different positions. There are two types of strip:

An unmarked strip. The elastic band indicates the positions of numbers on the strips

- a blank strip with no markings

- a strip divided into 10 equal parts.

A strip marked off into 10 divisions

Classroom resources

A few commonly available resources are mentioned in the activity notes, with simple alternatives given where appropriate. The following are the main resources required.

- 2D and 3D shapes   Any commercial sets of 2D and 3D shapes for teaching about shapes. The Polygon Allsorts from NES Arnold have been specially designed to provide the rich variety of shapes needed.

- Geostrips   These have brass fasteners and are useful for shape and angle work.

- Counters

Ready-made resources

Number cards are available from Ginn & Co., Linacre House, Jordan Hill, Oxford OX2 8DP.

The following resources are also available from NES Arnold, Ludlow Hill Road, West Bridgford, Nottingham, NG2 6HD:

- counting sticks
- swinging apple for counting pendulum
- number fans

- arrow cards; small and large
- number strips and bands
- number lines and grids.

Using counting patterns

Purpose	To continue, develop and use counting skills on a wide range of numbers.
Development	Counting on and back in small numbers to an increasing range of numbers

Thigh clap *Continuing a counting sequence by 10, 100 and 1000 forward and back*

Pupils sit on chairs.

◆ Play *Thigh, clap, snap, snap*. Pupils gently slap the top of their thighs with both hands, followed by a clap of both hands. They then snap their fingers, first with one hand, then with the other. If they find snapping difficult, they can wave with alternate hands instead. Once a rhythm is steady, pupils count on from different starting numbers in unison. They say the number on the 'thigh' action – the 'clap, snap, snap' actions allow for thinking time and also provide time to say the numbers. Set a suitable tempo for the actions, slowing down or speeding up as appropriate.

Choose suitable starting numbers from which to count forward in tens, hundreds and thousands.

◆ Repeat the previous activity, but count back in tens, hundreds and thousands.

Pendulum count *Counting forward and back*

You will need: a long piece of string with a weight attached to make a pendulum. Fasten the pendulum so that it swings freely and pupils can count in time with the swings. This sets up a counting rhythm for pupils to match. The string of the pendulum can be lengthened or shortened to alter the rate of swing. Pupils count on alternate swings. Extend to counting on each swing if it seems appropriate.

◆ Pupils watch the pendulum swing and count forward and back in tens, hundreds and thousands from different numbers. Vary the length of the counting sequence.

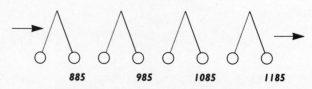

Counting forward in hundreds

◆ Pupils count forward and back in small number steps from a range of numbers. Include counting back beyond zero.

◆ Pupils count forward and back in twenty-fives and multiples of ten from a range of numbers.

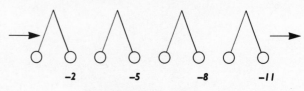

Counting back in threes

Sound jumps *Counting forward and back in small steps*

Pupils sit in three large groups.

◆ Explain that they are going to hear some sound jumps, like someone jumping along a number track. They say on which number the jump lands. Make the 'jump' sound by snapping your fingers and a 'landing' sound by clapping your hands. Pause after each jump for the pupils to say the landing numbers in unison. Say the size of the jump. For example, start on 175 and make jumps of three:

175	*178*	*181*	*184*
(snap, clap)	(snap, clap)	(snap, clap)	

Repeat, using different sizes of jump, within an appropriate number range. Include counting back to below zero:

2	*–3*	*–8*	*–13*
(snap, clap)	(snap, clap)	(snap, clap)	

◆ Repeat the activity with the groups taking turns to say the next number landed on. For example, start on 22 and jump forward by five:

group 1 **27**   *group 2* **32**   *group 3* **37**   *group 1* **42**   *group 2* **47**   *group 3* **52**

(snap, clap)   (snap, clap)   (snap, clap)   (snap, clap)   (snap, clap)

Dead stop *Counting forward and back in jumps of ones, tens, hundreds and thousands*

Pupils count in unison. Set a tempo for the counting sequence by: leading the count, clapping, finger wagging, using a metronome...

◆ Pupils count forward or back in unison within an appropriate number range. They stop when they have counted a certain number of jumps. For example, counting back 6000 from 7250 in jumps of 1000.

◆ Similar to the previous activity, but this time give pupils starting and finishing numbers and size of jump. Independently, they count within these numbers, then say how many jumps have been counted. For example:

Jump on from 737 to 817 in tens. How many tens?
Jump back from 2133 to 1533. How many hundreds?

Thigh clap *Counting in halves*

Pupils sit on chairs.

◆ Play *Thigh, clap, snap, snap*. Choose suitable starting numbers from which to count forward and back by halves. Pupils count in unison on the 'snap snap' action.

thigh   clap   snap   snap   thigh   clap   snap   snap   thigh

$7\frac{1}{2}$ 8 $8\frac{1}{2}$ 9

Number facts to 20

> **Purpose**   To learn by heart all the number bonds and trios to 20. They also learn all doubles and halves within 20, and that addition and subtraction are inverses. You should expect immediate responses.

Number cards *Number facts and language to about 20*

**You will need: a set of number cards (page 40) for each pupil.
Ask pupils to arrange the cards in front of them so that they can find the numbers easily.**

◆ Pupils hold up number cards to play *Show me* with number facts to about 20. Pupil should respond fairly rapidly. For example:

Show me the total of: 5 and 7, 9 and 6, 4 and 7...
Show me the sum of: 3, 6 and 4,   7, 5 and 8,   5, 7 and 5...
Show me double: 9, 6, $7\frac{1}{2}$...
Show me a half of: 14, 11, 18...
What is 4 more than (less than): 20, 17, $11\frac{1}{2}$...?
What is: 19 take away 9? 16 minus 9?
The difference between 18 and 13?
Show me two odd numbers which total: 18, 12, 14...

**Showing 12 with
number cards**

Chain sums *Quick calculations with 3 or more numbers, and different operations*

You will need: a set of number cards (page 40) for each pupil. Ask pupils to arrange the cards in front of them so that they can find the numbers easily. Pupils sit with their eyes closed.

◆ Give a chain sum such as: $4 + 7 - 2, 17 - 5 + 6, 20 - 5 - 8...$

At the end of the chain they open their eyes and hold up number cards to show their answer. In the chain include language such as 'total', 'sum', 'double', 'half'. Include table facts such as $3 \times 5 + 7, 19 - 14 \times 2, 49 \div 7 + 5...$ within the chain.

◆ Place the chain sum in a context such as passengers getting on and off buses, coins being gained and lost. Extend the chain sum to include more than three numbers.

Ping pong *Number pairs to 20, doubles and halves*

The class is 'halved' into two teams, preferably sitting in a large circle. Questions and answers will ping pong between the two teams. Choose who gives the starting number and who responds, so that each team has its share of going first, and so that all pupils take part.

◆ Choose a member from one team to give any number in the 0–20 range. Then choose a member from the opposing team to give the complement which makes 20. They can use numbers such as $8\frac{1}{2}$.

◆ Repeat the previous activity for halving and doubling numbers.

Shape totals *Totalling 3 or more numbers within 20*

You will need: a set of number cards (page 40) for each pupil. Ask pupils to arrange the cards in front of them so that they can find the numbers easily.

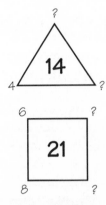

The corner numbers must total
the middle number

◆ Draw a triangle on the board with a teen number in the centre. Explain that there should be numbers at each corner of the triangle, which should add up to the number in the middle. Write one corner number on the triangle and ask pupils to hold up number cards to show what the other two numbers could be. Discuss alternatives. For example, with a centre number of 14 and a given corner number of 4, the missing two corner numbers must total 10. Include halves, such as having a corner number of $7\frac{1}{2}$.

◆ Repeat the activity, but change the shape to a square. Give two corner numbers and ask pupils to work out the others. Repeat, giving one corner number only. Discuss strategies they could use. Increase the centre number to beyond 20.

◆ Repeat the previous activities, placing a small negative number, such as –8 in the centre of a shape.

Tell me about *Number facts to about 20*

Pupils sit on chairs.

◆ Give a number and ask each pupil to give a different fact about it. Pupils take turns to answer and the answers should ripple quickly round the class with no exact repeats. For example, the number 17:

It is the total of 8 and 9, it is half 34, it is $16\frac{1}{2}$ plus $\frac{1}{2}$, it is 20 minus 3...

Guess my number *Number facts*

You will need: a set of number cards (page 40) for each pupil. Ask pupils to arrange the cards in front of them so that they can find the numbers easily.

◆ Think of a number 0–20, such as 13; do not reveal the number. The aim is to avoid the number being guessed for as long as possible. Give one fact about the number. *It is odd.* Pupils try to guess the number and hold up number cards to show possible answers. Provide further facts about the number, one by one, with number cards being shown after each fact.

It is a prime number. It is greater than ten.
It is less than fifteen. Its digits total four.

Encourage pupils to look at each other's cards and to think of alternatives. Eventually every pupil should be holding up the same number.

Place value

Purpose	To develop ideas of place value to at least 7-digit numbers. Pupils can call the right hand digit 'ones' or 'units'. Pupils should feel comfortable with large numbers. They should know that k = 1000.

Place value grid *Place value and extended notation*

You will need: seven counters and a place value grid (page 41) for each pupil.

◆ Explain how to use counters on the grid to represent numbers. Give a series of numbers for pupils to show on their grids.

◆ Ask pupils to make the largest odd number which is less than 1 million using only three counters. Then ask them to make the smallest even number. Check they have made 990 009 and 112.

Similarly, ask them to make numbers such as: multiples of 5, multiples of 10, odd numbers between 50 000 and 1 000 000...

10 000 000	20 000 000	30 000 000	40 000 000	50 000 000	60 000 000	70 000 000	80 000 000	90 000 000
1 000 000	2 000 000	3 000 000	4 000 000	5 000 000	6 000 000	7 000 000	8 000 000	9 000 000
100 000	200 000	300 000	400 000	500 000 ●	600 000	700 000	800 000	900 000
10 000	20 000	30 000	40 000	50 000	60 000	70 000	80 000	90 000
1000	2000	3000	4000	5000	6000	7000	8000	9000 ●
100	200	300	400	500	600	700	800	900
10	20	30 ●	40	50	60	70	80	90
1	2	3	4	5	6	7 ●	8	9

The counters show the number 500 937

Counting stick *Positions on a number line*

You will need: a strip of wood, about one metre long, divided into ten equal sections. An unnumbered decimetre metre stick is ideal.

◆ Name one end of the stick as zero and the other end as 1000. Point to the middle and ask which number would go there. Then point to different divisions on the stick and ask the same question.

◆ Repeat the previous activity, naming one end of the stick as zero and the other end as 10 000, 100 000, 1 000 000 in turn.

Hands up *Number facts*

Pupils sit on chairs. Explain that if the statement you make is true, they should hold their hands up high in the air. If it is false, they should place both hands flat on the table, or on their knees.

◆ Choose a range of number facts to which pupils should be able to respond rapidly. Include statements such as:

Ten thousand has four zeros. One million has seven zeros.
Double ten thousand is one million. Fifteen k is less than ten thousand.
Half of a million is fifty thousand. Ten times a hundred is a thousand.
A hundred times a hundred is one hundred thousand.

Elastic band strips *Position of numbers*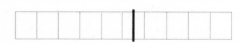

You will need: a strip of card for each pupil, which they mark off into ten equal sections. They slide an elastic band onto the strip, taut enough not to drop off.

◆ Tell pupils that one end of the strip is zero and the other end is 10 000. Ask them to slide the elastic band along to where they think 5500 would be. They hold up their responses.

A strip marked off into 10 divisions

Ask pupils to show the position of numbers such as: 9500, 6000, 8500...

◆ Repeat the previous activity but with one end of the strip as zero and the other end as 100 000. Pupils move their elastic bands to show numbers such as: 90 000, 45 000, 20 000, 75 000...

Number generator *Place value and number properties*

You will need: a number generator (page 42) for each pupil.

◆ Choose numbers at random and ask pupils to show them. Extend the activity to showing numbers with particular properties.

Show me a number between 20 000 and 25 000.
Show me an odd number greater than 90 000.

◆ Ask pupils to show numbers which are 1 less than numbers ending in zero, such as: 300, 9000, 7500, 80 000...

◆ Ask pupils to show numbers which are 1 more than numbers ending in nine, such as: 799, 6599, 8999, 40 199...

◆ Ask pupils to show the result of multiplying and dividing by powers of 10.

Show me: 700 × 100, 550 000 ÷ 1000...

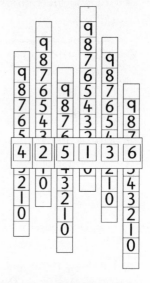

A number made on a number generator

Number generator *Place value and number properties*

Pupils work in co-operating groups of about five or six.
You will need: a number generator (page 42) for each pupil. Tell pupils how many strips they will need in their generators.

◆ Each pupil in each group makes a different number on their generator.

Who in the group has an odd number? Who has a multiple of 5?
Who has the number nearest to 75 000? Who has the largest number?

Ask pupils to arrange their numbers in order.

Rounding, equality and inequality

Purpose	To round, estimate and approximate numbers. They also use the symbols <, > and ≈. The number range should include negative numbers, positive numbers, fractions and decimals.

Elastic band strips *Estimation and position of numbers*

You will need: two strips of card for each pupil, one of which they mark off into ten equal sections. They slide elastic bands onto the strips, taut enough not to drop off.

◆ Tell pupils that one end of the strip is zero and the other is 1000. Ask them to slide the elastic band along to where they think 350 would be. They hold up their responses.

Similarly, ask them to show the position of numbers such as: 850, 150, 650...
Extend to numbers such as: 624, 991, 816...
Discuss the nearest 10 and nearest 100 for each number.

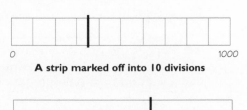

A strip marked off into 10 divisions

An unmarked strip. The elastic band indicates the positions of numbers on the strip

◆ Change the value of the strips. For example, the ends being zero and 10 000, and ask pupils to round to the nearest thousand and ten thousand.

◆ Repeat the previous activity using the unmarked strip. Include negative numbers such as zero to –10 and zero to –100.

◆ Using a marked or unmarked strip, tell pupils that one end of the strip is zero and the other end is 1. Ask pupils to slide the elastic band along to approximate to: quarters, fifths, tenths, eighths... and to 0.3, 0.7, 0.9...

◆ Repeat the activity, using number ranges such as: 750 to 850, 2600 to 2700, –50 to +50...

Number generator *Rounding*

You will need: a number generator (page 42) for each pupil. Depending on the number range you are using, tell pupils how many strips they will need in their generators.

◆ Choose numbers at random and ask pupils to round them to the nearest: ten, hundred, thousand.

◆ Talk about rounding up and rounding down and how this might vary from rounding off. For instance, 5249 rounded up to the 'next hundred' is 5300, rounded down to the 'next hundred' is 5200, but rounded off to the 'nearest hundred' it is 5200. Give pupils numbers to round up and then round down.

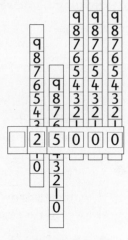

Rounding 24 560 to the nearest thousand

Inequality signs *Using >, < and ≈ signs*

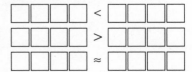

You will need: a shuffled set of large number cards. On the board draw three grids like these and ask pupils to copy them. The sign between the digit boxes will be >, < or ≈ .

◆ Ask each pupil to draw a grid using the sign <. Turn over the top number card. Pupils decide where on their grid to write the number. Turn over seven more number cards for pupils to record on their grids. The aim is to make the statement true when their grid is complete. Discuss pupil results. Repeat this game using the > sign.

◆ Repeat the first game using the ≈ sign. Explain that the two numbers should be as close together as possible.

◆ Play the three games again, but returning the first number card to the pack and reshuffling before turning over the next card.

Tell me about *Position and approximation of number and measures*

Pupils sit on chairs.

◆ On the board write two numbers, amounts of money or measures. Discuss which numbers or measures could come between these two. Talk about responses which are nearer to one number than the other. Use the > and < symbols as appropriate.

$7550 < \boxed{} < 8000$

$4.0\,kg > \boxed{} > 2.5\,kg$

$£75.89 ≈ \boxed{}$

Tell me about which numbers can go in the boxes

◆ On the board write a number or measurement which is followed by the ≈ sign. Discuss which number or measure could follow this sign. Also talk about when a number stops being 'approximately the same as'. Talk about when we would round to the nearest: whole number, ten, hundred...

Counting stick *Estimating positions on a number line and rounding*

You will need: a strip of wood, about one metre long, divided into ten equal sections. An unnumbered decimetre metre stick is ideal.

◆ Name one end of the stick as zero and the other as 1000. Point to an intermediate position and ask which number would go there. Then point to different random positions on the stick and ask the same question. Ask which hundreds number is nearest and discuss rounding. Repeat for the number range zero to 10 000, rounding to the nearest thousand.

About 320

◆ Use decimals by naming one end of the stick as zero and the other as 1. Point to random divisions for pupils to name: 0.3, 0.6, 0.8. Then point to midway between divisions for: 0.45, 0.95, 0.55...

About 0.45

Mental calculations

Purpose	To use several mental strategies to solve calculations. The calculations here can be answered fairly quickly.
Development	Giving approximate answers.

Number generator *Calculations with multiples of 10*

You will need: a number generator (page 42) for each pupil.

◆ Give a range of additions and subtractions for multiples of 10 appropriate for the pupils. They solve them mentally and hold up their generators to show the answer. Use a variety of number language in the activity. For example:

Show me the sum of 140 and 520. Show me the difference between 540 and 90. Total 360 and 250. Subtract 520 from 940.

◆ Repeat the activity with multiplication and division facts.

Show me the product of 40 and 80. Show me 2400 divided by 30. Show me the quotient to 120 divided by 20.

◆ Repeat the previous activity but extend to multiples of 50 which total 1000.

Show me what must be added to these numbers to make 1000: 750, 350, 650...

Ping pong *Doubles and halves*

The class is 'halved' into two teams. Choose who gives the starting numbers and who responds, so that all pupils participate.

◆ Choose a member from one team to double a number between 1 and 100.

I know that double 48 is 96. Which double do you know?

Choose a member from the opposing team to respond. They could respond:

I know that double 25 is 50. Which double do you know?

◆ Repeat the previous activity but extend to doubling multiples of 10 to 1000 and doubling multiples of 100 to 10 000.

I know double 630 is 1260. Which double do you know?
I know double 5200 is 10 400. Which double do you know?

◆ Repeat the previous activities for corresponding halves.

Number cards *Close differences; totalling three 2-digit numbers*

You will need: a set of number cards (page 40), without the $\frac{1}{2}$s, for each pupil.

◆ Choose a pair of appropriate close numbers and ask pupils to hold up number cards to show the difference between the two numbers. Discuss strategies, e.g. counting on or back. Gradually increase the number size.

◆ Give pupils three 2-digit numbers to total and show their answers. If it will help, write the three numbers on the board.

Number generator *Approximating calculations*

You will need: a number generator (page 42) for each pupil.

◆ Discuss rounding to the nearest 10, 100 and 1000 and how this can help in checking for mistakes in calculations. For example, rounding 897 + 319 to 900 + 300. Ask pupils to round sums and show approximations. Include addition, subtraction and multiplication approximations.

◆ Repeat the previous activity using division, but give it special consideration. A calculation such as 239 ÷ 28 can be rounded to 200 ÷ 30, but this then needs a second approximation of 20 ÷ 3 in order to find the approximate quotient.

Fan numbers *Calculations with 2-digit numbers*

Pupils work in co-operating pairs, or threes. You will need: a set of fan numbers (page 43), without the decimal point, for each pupil.

◆ Using the number fans, ask each pupil to make a 2-digit number so that the total from each pair is: 100, 108, 122... Extend to a mix of 2-digit and 3-digit numbers.

◆ Ask each pupil to make a 2-digit number so that the difference between the numbers in each pair is: 4, 29, 43... Extend to a mix of 2-digit and 3-digit numbers.

Fan numbers totalling 100

◆ Ask each pupil to make a 2-digit number so that the product from each pair is: 150, 240, 144...

Place value grid *Counting through multiples of 10, 100 and 1000*

You will need: a place value grid (page 41) and some counters for each pupil.

◆ Remind pupils how to use counters on the grid to represent numbers. Ask pupils what must be added to a range of numbers to round them to the next 10, 100, 1000 and 10 000. Pupils place counters on their place value grids to match the answer.

What must be added to 4750 to round it to 10 000?

10000000	20000000	30000000	40000000	50000000	60000000	70000000	80000000	90000000
1000000	2000000	3000000	4000000	5000000	6000000	7000000	8000000	9000000
100000	200000	300000	400000	500000	600000	700000	800000	900000
10000	20000	30000	40000	50000	60000	70000	80000	90000
1000	2000	●3000	4000	5000	6000	7000	8000	9000
●100	200	300	400	500	600	700	800	900
10	20	30	40	●50	60	70	80	90
1	2	3	4	●5	6	7	8	9

Counters placed to show 7000 – 3845

◆ Explain how to count through multiples of 10, 100 and 1000 to answer sums such as 7000 – 3665. Then give similar examples for pupils to show answers by placing counters on their grids.

Quick answers

Purpose	To highlight some of the quick answers which pupils should calculate or know. These include calculations such as adding and subtracting 9, 19, 29… and 11, 21, 31… as well as adding, subtracting, multiplying by and dividing by powers of 10. Equivalences of measurements and money are included, as are simple percentages.

Cycle cards *Number and measurement facts*

You will need: one or more cycle cards for each pupil. Each cycle card has two parts to it, an answer and a question. The question on one cycle card has its answer on another. Within a set of cycle cards, each answer should be unique to avoid two pupils calling out the same answer. Sets of cycle cards can have a theme, such as adding 99 or finding simple percentages. They can also be general facts which pupils can answer quickly.

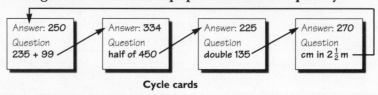

Cycle cards

◆ One pupil starts the cycle:

My question is: What is 235 + 99?

The pupil with the card showing the answer replies and asks their question:

I have the answer: 334. My question is: What is half of 450?

Questions and answers should ripple around the classroom fairly quickly until the cycle is complete. Redistribute the cards and repeat the activity.

Hands up *Number facts*

Pupils sit on chairs. If the statement you make is true, they should hold their hands up high in the air. If it is false, they place both hands on the table, or on their knees.

◆ Choose number statements to which pupils should respond rapidly.

*These are odd numbers: 467, 1350, 14 675… These are multiples of 9: 99, 162, 334…
These total 1000: 400 + 600, 550 + 750, 350 + 650…
There are: 50 centimetres in half a metre, 500 kilograms in half a tonne, 50 millilitres in half a litre…*

Pass it on *Quick calculations with powers of 10*

Pupils sit on chairs.

◆ From a starting number, pupils add or subtract 1, 10, 100 or 1000. They can also multiply or divide by 10, 100 or 1000. The pupil chooses what to do to the number before passing it on to the next person. For example:

*250, I add on 10 and pass it on. 260, I multiply by 10 and pass it on.
2600, I subtract 100 and pass it on. 2500, I subtract 1 and pass it on…*

Decide whether to have a number limit which must not be passed.

Ping pong *Adding and subtracting 9 and 99/Other simple additions and subtractions*

The class is 'halved' into two teams, preferably sitting in a large circle. Choose who gives the starting number, and who responds, so that you can match the question with the ability to answer and everyone has a turn.

◆ Choose one team member to give any number and say whether 9 is to be added to or subtracted from that number.

I choose 427 and I want you to add on 9.

Choose a member from the opposing team to answer.

The answer is 436. I want you to subtract 9 from 1000.

Repeat, adding and subtracting 99 to and from a range of numbers.

◆ Extend to using other additions and subtractions such as 19, 29, 11, 21…

Tell me about *Equivalence, time, measurements and money*

Pupils sit on chairs.

◆ Choose a measurement such as 2.5 metres. Invite pupils to give a range of facts about that measurement. Initially, you may need to prompt them:
  - equivalences such as 250 cm, 2500 mm, $2\frac{1}{2}$ metres.
  - estimations such as, it is about the same height as the door.
  - positions such as, it lies halfway between 2 metres and 3 metres.

Use measurements of length, weight and capacity and money equivalences.

◆ Ask pupils to suggest items they would measure in mm, pints, g, km, tonnes…

◆ Ask pupils to suggest appropriate metric units to measure items such as: the length of the classroom, the capacity of a teacup, the distance between two towns, the thickness of a workbook… Include prefixes such as deci, centi, milli and talk about measures such as decilitres and decimetres.

◆ Discuss time facts and calculations, e.g. minutes/hour, how long between two times.

Thigh clap *Quick calculations*

Pupils sit on chairs.

◆ Play *Thigh, clap, snap, snap.* Pupils gently slap the top of their thighs with both hands, followed by a clap of both hands. They then snap their fingers, first with one hand, then with the other. If they find snapping difficult, they can wave with alternate hands instead. Once a rhythm is steady, pupils count on from different starting numbers in unison. Pupils count in unison on the 'snap snap' action.

Choose suitable starting numbers from which pupils add or subtract small numbers, such as 1, 10, 9, 11, 2, 3, 5.

thigh clap snap snap thigh clap snap snap thigh

325 335   345 355

Table facts

Purpose	To use all the multiplication facts, and associated division facts, to 10×10.
Development	Using known table facts and knowledge of place value to calculate sums such as 60×70. You may need to emphasize the facts which cause most problems: $8 \times 6, 7 \times 9, 8 \times 7, 4 \times 9, 9 \times 6, 8 \times 8, 7 \times 6, 8 \times 4, 7 \times 7$ and 9×4.

Number cards *Multiplication and division facts*

You will need: a set of number cards (page 40) for each pupil.

Show me 3 x 9

◆ Play *Show me*, where pupils hold up two number cards to make 2-digit answers. Ask a range of multiplication facts.

Show me the answer to: $8 \times 6, 6 \times 4, 7 \times 7, 9 \times 6, 8 \times 8$...
What is the product of: 9 and 8, 6 and 7, 5 and 3...?
Show me a common multiple of: 7 and 5, 4 and 7, 3 and 8...

◆ Repeat the previous activity, asking a range of division facts.

Show me the answer to: $72 \div 9, 36 \div 4, 42 \div 7$...
Show me how many eights are in: 72, 32, 56...   Show me a factor of: 45, 56, 81...

Thigh clap *Multiples*

Pupils sit on chairs.

◆ Play *Thigh, clap, snap, snap*. Pupils gently slap the top of their thighs with both hands, followed by a clap of both hands. They then snap their fingers, first with one hand, then with the other. If they find snapping difficult, they can wave with alternate hands instead. Once a rhythm is steady, pupils count from different starting numbers in unison. They count on the 'snap snap' action.

Pupils count forward in different multiples such as 6, 7, 8 and 9, continuing the count beyond the tenth multiple.

◆ Repeat the previous activity, but counting back in different multiples.

Fan numbers *Multiplication and division facts*

You will need: a set of fan numbers (page 43), without the decimal point, for each pupil.

◆ Using the number fans, play *Show me*, about multiplication and division.

Show me the answer to: $9 \times 7, 54 \div 6, 8 \times 4$...

Use language such as multiple, product, quotient, square...

◆ Repeat the previous activity, but show the result of multiplications beyond the tenth multiple. *You know 10×6. Show me 12×6. You know 10×3. Show me 11×3.*

Multiplication square *Multiplication and division facts*

You will need: a copy of a 10 × 10 multiplication square, and some counters, for each pupil.

◆ Ask pupils to place a counter to show the answer to a multiplication such as: 6 × 7, 9 × 9, 7 × 3...

◆ Ask pupils to place counters on squares to show the answer to a division such as: 48 ÷ 6, 64 ÷ 8, 72 ÷ 9...

◆ Choose a number in the square, such as 56. Ask pupils to place a counter on one of the '56' numbers on the grid and to say some facts about the 56 they have chosen, such as 7 × 8, 8 × 7, 56 ÷ 7 and 56 ÷ 8. Repeat for other numbers in the square.

Discuss the numbers along the diagonal that are square numbers.

×	1	2	3	4	5	6	7	8	9	10
1	1	2	3	4	5	6	7	8	9	10
2	2	4	6	8	10	12	14	16	18	20
3	3	6	9	12	15	18	21	24	27	30
4	4	8	12	16	20	24	28	32	36	40
5	5	10	15	20	25	30	35	40	45	50
6	6	12	18	24	30	36	●	48	54	60
7	7	14	21	28	35	42	49	56	63	70
8	8	16	24	32	40	48	56	64	72	80
9	9	18	27	36	45	54	63	72	81	90
10	10	20	30	40	50	60	70	80	90	100

Multiplication square showing 6 x 7

Thigh clap *Multiples*

Pupils sit on chairs.

◆ Play *Thigh, clap, snap, snap*. Once a rhythm is steady, pupils count on from different starting numbers in unison on each action. If this is too challenging, change to counting on the 'thigh' action. Ask pupils to count forward. When they reach 7 or a multiple of 7 they say 'buzz' instead of the number word. This can be played as a game with pupils taking turns to say the next number. Play *Buzz* for other multiples.

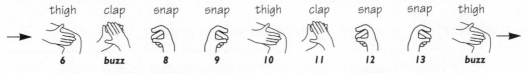

thigh	clap	snap	snap	thigh	clap	snap	snap	thigh
6	buzz	8	9	10	11	12	13	buzz

◆ Extend the activity to include saying 'fizz' – for 4 or a multiple of 4.

One, two, three, fizz, five, six, buzz, fizz, nine, ten, eleven, fizz, thirteen, buzz...

When they reach a number which is a multiple of both 7 and 4, they say 'fizz-buzz'. Play *Fizz-buzz* for other pairs of multiples.

◆ As a challenge, play *Fizz-buzz* counting backwards.

Number cards *Using divisibility rules and finding remainders*

You will need: a set of number cards (page 40) for each pupil.

◆ Discuss divisibility rules for 2, 3, 5, 9 and 10 and possible remainders when dividing by the numbers 2 to 10. Explain how to count on from multiples to find the remainder. Using the number cards, play *Show me*, asking pupils for the remainders.

Show me the remainder when I divide these numbers by five: 17, 25, 46, 32...
Show me the remainder when I divide these numbers by ten: 52, 40, 64, 78...
Show me the remainder when I divide these numbers by six: 17, 25, 39, 66...

Extending multiplication and division

Purpose	To use multiplication and division facts combined with ideas of place value to extend the use of multiplication and division tables. Strategies include using the number bond then adjusting for zeros and using known facts, or easier techniques, to answer calculations.

Number generator *Extending multiplication and division*

You will need: a number generator (page 42) for each pupil.

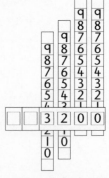

◆ Give a range of multiplications for multiples of 10 for pupils to answer.

Show me the product of 40 and 80.
Show me 70 multiplied by 60.
Show me: 600 × 80, 50 × 7000, 800 × 800.

◆ Give a range of divisions for multiples of 10 for pupils to answer.

Show me 2400 divided by 60. Show me the quotient to 120 divided by 30.
Show me: 6400 ÷ 80, 72 000 ÷ 800, 8100 ÷ 900.

Showing the answer to 40 × 80

Hands up *Multiplication, division and place value*

Pupils sit on chairs. If the statement you make is true, they hold their hands in the air. If it is false, they place both hands on the table, or their knees.

◆ Choose a range of number statements to which pupils should be able to respond rapidly. Include statements such as:

The answer to 80 × 70 is 560. The answer to 500 × 40 is 20 000.
The answer to 25 000 ÷ 50 is 500. The answer to 5600 ÷ 80 is 7.

◆ Play *Endings* where pupils have to work out how many zeros a calculation will have.

40 × 60 ends in two zeros. 700 × 400 ends in five zeros.
2000 ÷ 40 ends in two zeros. 6300 ÷ 900 ends in one zero.

Fan numbers *Multiplication and division facts*

Pupils sit on chairs.
You will need: a set of fan numbers (page 43), without the decimal point, for each pupil.

◆ Ask pupils to hold up the number fans to answer questions about multiplication and division facts.

Show me the answer to 90 × 7, 540 ÷ 6, 80 × 40...

Use language such as multiple, product, quotient, square...

Show me 6 x 80

◆ Repeat the previous activity, but ask pupils to show the result of multiplications beyond the tenth multiple.

You know 10 × 6. Now show me 15 × 6.
You know 10 × 8. Now show me 12 × 8.

Place value grid *Multiplying and dividing by powers of 10*

You will need: a place value grid (page 41) and some counters, for each pupil.

◆ Remind pupils how to use counters on the grid to represent numbers. Ask pupils to place counters on their grid to make a number such as 536 and then to multiply it by 10, 100 or 1000, showing the new number on the grid. Discuss the shift upwards of the digits when multiplying by powers of 10. Repeat for other numbers.

◆ Repeat the previous activity but ask pupils to make a number such as 72 000 and then to divide it by 10, 100 or 1000. Discuss the shift downward of the digits when dividing by powers of 10. Repeat for other numbers.

10000000	20000000	30000000	40000000	50000000	60000000	70000000	80000000	90000000
1000000	2000000	3000000	4000000	5000000	6000000	7000000	8000000	9000000
100000	200000	300000	400000	500000	600000	700000	800000	900000
10000	20000	30000	40000	50000	60000	70000	80000	90000
1000	2000	3000	4000	● 5000	6000	7000	8000	9000
100	200	● 300	400	500	600	700	800	900
10	20	30	40	50	● 60	70	80	90
1	2	3	4	5	6	7	8	9

Counters placed to show 536 × 10.

Number cards *Mental calculation techniques for multiplication*

You will need: a set of number cards (page 40) for each pupil.

◆ Using the number cards, play *Show me*, asking pupils to show 16 × facts by doubling 8 ×.

Show me 4 × 8. Now show me 4 × 16.
Show me 7 × 8. Now show me 7 × 16.

◆ Repeat for other 16 × multiplications. Extend to similar 'doubling' calculations, such as for 12 ×, 14 × and 18 × (double 6 ×, 7 ×, and 9 ×, respectively).

◆ Explain how in a multiplication one number can be doubled and the other halved without changing the answer. For example, 16 × 6 is equivalent to 32 × 3 or 8 × 12.

Show me 18 × 8. Show me 14 × 12. Show me 24 × 6.

Number cards *Mental calculation techniques for division*

You will need: a set of number cards (page 40) for each pupil.

◆ Using the number cards, play *Show me*, asking pupils to show ÷6 facts by halving both numbers to make it ÷3. Pupils should hold their number cards with their answers close to their chests until told to show them.

96 ÷ 6 is the same as 48 ÷ 3.

Explain how ÷8 can be found by halving and halving again.

96 ÷ 8 = 48 ÷ 4 = 24 ÷ 2 = 12.

Give further division problems for pupils to solve. Discuss techniques.

Special numbers

<table>
<tr><td>Purpose</td><td>To use special number terms, such as prime, square, square root, factor, odd, even. Pupils should know the squares of 1 to 10 and the corresponding square roots. They should also know about prime numbers including 2-digit primes. Pupils should be able to state factors of numbers up to 100.</td></tr>
</table>

Number cards *Square, square root, prime, factor, odd and even, multiple*

Show me a prime factor of 42

You will need: a set of number cards (page 40) for each pupil.

◆ Ensure that pupils know what square numbers are and their square roots. Play *Show me*, asking facts about square numbers and square roots. Discuss alternative answers to the questions.

Show me a square number greater than 50. Show me an odd square number.
Show me a square number which is a multiple of 5. Show me the square root of 36.

◆ Ensure that pupils know what prime numbers are. Play *Show me*, asking facts about prime numbers.

Show me a prime number which is more than 20. Show me an even prime number.
Show me a prime number between 20 and 50.

◆ Ensure that pupils know what a factor is. Play *Show me*, asking pupils to show factors of: 24, 56, 98, 38... Extend to problems such as:

Show me a prime factor of 36. Show me an odd factor of 48.

Hands up *Odd and even*

Pupils sit on chairs. If the statement you make is true, they hold their hands in the air. If it is false, they place both hands on the table, or on their knees.

◆ Discuss how 'odd + odd = even', 'odd × odd = odd', 'even − even = even'...
Then choose a range of statements which pupils can answer rapidly.

9 × 5 gives an even answer. The total of 667 and 512 will be odd.
The product of 35 and 62 will be even.
The difference between 934 and 441 will be even.
The sum of 755 and 526 will be odd. The square of 27 will be odd.

Ping pong *Square numbers, square roots, odd and even*

The class is 'halved' into two teams, preferably sitting in a large circle. Questions and answers will ping pong between the two teams. Choose who gives the starting number and who responds, so that you can match the question with the ability to answer and each team member has a turn.

◆ Choose one team member to give any number in the 0–10 range.
Then choose a member in the opposing team to give the square of this number. Encourage speedy responses to the questions.

I give you 9 – please square it. I give you 64 – please tell me the square root.

Repeat for different numbers.

Fan numbers *Number language*

You will need: a set of fan numbers (page 43), without the decimal point, for each pupil.

◆ Using the number fans, play *Show me* activities which use different number language. Discuss alternative answers.

Show me an odd multiple of 7. Show me an even factor of 56.
Show me a prime factor of 32. Show me the square of 7.
Show me the difference between –5 and 4. Show me the product of 40 and 60.
Show me the quotient of 270 divided by 10. Show me four dozen.

Thigh clap *Prime numbers*

Pupils sit on chairs.

◆ Play *Thigh, clap, snap, snap*. Pupils gently slap the top of their thighs with both hands, followed by a clap of both hands. They then snap their fingers, first with one hand, then with the other. If they find snapping difficult, they can wave with alternate hands instead. Pupils count in unison on each action. If this is too challenging, change to counting on the 'thigh' action.

Ask pupils to count forward. When they reach a prime number they say 'buzz' instead of the number word. This can be played as a game with pupils taking turns to say the next number.

Number cards *Factors*

You will need: a set of number cards (page 40) for each pupil.

◆ Pupils hold up number cards to play *Show me*. Ask pupils questions such as: If x is a factor of a number, show me another factor. For example, if 6 is a factor of a number, pupils could show 3 or 2.

If 12 is a factor of a number then show me another.

Check pupils are holding up 1, 2, 3, 4 or 6.

If 9 is a factor then show me another.

This time only 1 or 3 are possibilities. Repeat for different numbers.

◆ Play *Show me*, asking pupils to find common factors.

Show me a common factor of 12 and 15.
Show me a common factor of 24 and 36.

◆ Play the reverse of the previous activity. Discuss alternative answers.

If 3 and 4 are factors of a number, show me what the number could be.
If 6 and 9 are factors of a number, show me what the number could be.

Fractions

Purpose	To bring together several different aspects of fractions such as estimation, equivalence, ordering, halving and mixed numbers.

Elastic band strips *Estimation of fractions*

Pupils sit on chairs.
You will need: a strip of card for each pupil. They slide an elastic band onto the strip, taut enough not to drop off.

◆ Tell pupils that one end of the strip is zero and the other is 1. Ask pupils to slide the elastic band along to where they think $\frac{3}{5}$ would be. They hold up their responses.

Repeat for other fractions such as: $\frac{2}{3}$, $\frac{3}{4}$, $\frac{5}{8}$, $\frac{1}{10}$.

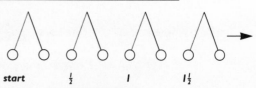

Show me $\frac{2}{3}$

◆ Ask pupils to show you fractions which are more, or less than stated fractions.

Show me a fraction which is a bit larger than: a half, three quarters, two thirds...
Show me a fraction which is just less than: a quarter, an eighth, three tenths...

Pendulum count *Forward in fractions*

You will need: a long piece of string with a weight attached to make a pendulum. Fasten the pendulum so that it swings freely and pupils can count in time with the swings. The string of the pendulum can be lengthened or shortened to alter the rate of swing. Pupils count on alternate swings. Extend to counting on each swing if it seems appropriate.

◆ Pupils watch the pendulum swing and count in halves on alternate swings.
Repeat the activity, counting in thirds and quarters, noting that two quarters make a half.

◆ Ask pupils to count in eighths, noting that two eighths make a quarter and four eighths a half.
Repeat for tenths or other similar fractions if appropriate.

start $\frac{1}{2}$ *1* $1\frac{1}{2}$
Counting in halves

Number cards *Equivalence of fractions to wholes*

You will need: a set of number cards (page 40) for each pupil.

◆ Pupils hold up number cards to play *Show me*. Ask pupils to show how many fractions make up a stated number of whole numbers. Pupils should hold the numbers cards with their answers close to their chests until told to show them. This will allow for thinking time.

Show me how many halves are in: 5, 9, 13...
Show me how many thirds are in: 6, 8, 11...
Show me how many tenths are in: 7, 12, 18...
Show me how many fifths are in: 3, 7, 10...

◆ Repeat the previous activity using fractions such as: $3\frac{1}{4}$, $5\frac{1}{2}$, $4\frac{2}{3}$...

INTERACTIVE MENTAL MATHS 5

Fractions

Fraction cards *Equivalence of common fractions*

You will need: a set of fraction cards (page 44) for each pupil.

◆ Play *Show me* with pupils showing a fraction card to answer language and equivalence questions.

Show me a fraction which is the same as: $\frac{1}{2}$, $\frac{1}{4}$, $\frac{3}{4}$...
Show me two fractions which are worth the same.
Show me a fraction more than a half, less than a third...

◆ Play *Show me* for the positions of fractions.

Show me a fraction which is half way between: 0 and 1, $\frac{1}{2}$ and $\frac{1}{4}$, $\frac{3}{4}$ and 1...
Show me a fraction between: $\frac{1}{8}$ and $\frac{3}{4}$, $\frac{1}{2}$ and $\frac{7}{8}$, $\frac{2}{3}$ and 1...

◆ Play *Show me* for complements of simple fractions to a whole.

What must be added to these to make a whole one? $\frac{3}{4}$, $\frac{2}{3}$, $\frac{5}{8}$, $\frac{3}{10}$...

As a challenge, include simple additions and subtractions, such as adding halves and quarters and subtracting simple fractions from a whole.

Number generator *Calculations with fractions*

You will need: a number generator (page 42) for each pupil.

◆ Ask pupils to find fractional amounts of numbers.

Show me $\frac{1}{2}$ of: 4800, 5000.

Repeat for other fractions such as $\frac{1}{3}$, $\frac{1}{4}$, $\frac{1}{5}$...

Extend to finding fractional amounts such as $\frac{2}{3}$ and $\frac{3}{4}$ where the numerator is greater than 1.

What is half of 6400?

◆ Ask pupils to find fractional amounts of measurements, such as:

How many centimetres in $\frac{3}{4}$ of 3 metres? How many grams in $\frac{3}{4}$ of 2 kilograms?
How many minutes in $\frac{3}{4}$ of an hour? What is $\frac{2}{3}$ of 1 kilometre in metres?

Ping pong *Equivalent fractions*

The class is 'halved' into two teams, preferably sitting in a large circle. Choose who gives the starting number, and who responds, match the question with the ability to answer and each team member has a turn.

◆ Choose a member from one team to say a fraction. Choose a member from the opposing team to give an equivalent fraction. The first team could find another equivalent fraction or you could choose a new fraction.

Decimals

Purpose	To use decimals to 2 places in the context of number and money.
Development	Learning about order, estimation and approximation of decimals as well as place value.

Decimal place value cards *Decimals to 2 places*

You will need: a set of decimal place value cards (page 45) for each pupil.

◆ Check that pupils know what tenths and hundredths are. Play *Show me* with pupils making decimal numbers such as:

Show me what five point two five looks like.
Show me six and a half.
Show me a decimal which has nine tenths.

Using decimal place value cards

◆ Play *Show me*, where pupils are given a range of decimals and asked to multiply or divide them by 10.

Decimal place value cards *Ordering decimals and decimal facts*

Pupils work in co-operating groups.
You will need: a set of decimal place value cards (page 45) for each pupil.

◆ Pupils play *Show me* in their groups, each person in the group making a different decimal number.

Who in the group has the number nearest to: 2.5, 7.25, 6, 0.5…?
Arrange your numbers in order. Who in the group has the largest (smallest) number?

Elastic band strips *Estimation of tenths*

You will need: a strip of card for each pupil. They slide an elastic band onto the strip, taut enough not to drop off.

◆ Tell pupils that one end of the strip is zero and the other is 1. Ask pupils to slide the elastic band along to where they think 0.6 would be. They hold up their responses. Ask pupils to show the position of other decimals such as: 0.2, 0.7, 0.5…

**A blank strip showing the
approximate position of 0.6**

Elastic band strips *Estimation of hundredths*

You will need: a strip of card for each pupil which they mark off into ten equal sections. They slide an elastic band onto the strip, taut enough not to drop off.

◆ Tell pupils that one end of the strip is zero and the other is 1. Ask pupils to slide the elastic band along to where they think 0.52 would be. Ask pupils to show the position of other decimals such as: 0.25, 0.78, 0.64…

**A strip marked off into ten equal divisions
showing the approximate position of 0.52**

Counting stick *Estimating decimals on a number line*

You will need: a strip of wood, about one metre long, divided into ten equal sections. An unnumbered decimetre metre stick is ideal.

◆ Name one end of the stick as zero and the other end as 1. Point to each division mark in turn, forward and back, asking which decimal goes there. Then point to random divisions and repeat. Pupils should respond fairly rapidly.

Position of tenths

◆ Point to intermediate positions between the division marks and ask which decimal number (hundredths) goes there.

Approximate position of hundredths

Fan numbers *Decimals*

Pupils work in co-operating groups.
You will need: a set of fan numbers (page 43) for each pupil. Ask the pupils to place the decimal point on top of the fan.

◆ Ask each group to make decimal numbers such as: 0.3, 0.25, 3.75, 0.02...

◆ Each group member makes a different decimal number. Ask questions such as:

Who in the group has: the largest (smallest) number, the number nearest to 2.5, a number greater than 5, a number less than 2?

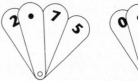

Decimal fan numbers

Decimal place value cards *Equivalence and notation of money*

You will need: a set of money cards for each pupil, made by adding the pounds sign (£) to a photocopy of the decimal place value cards (page 45). Ask pupils to arrange the cards in front of them so that they can find the numbers easily.

Money cards

◆ Ask pupils to use their money cards to show stated amounts. This will check they understand decimal notation when recording money.

Show me: £2.75, £5.40, £2.74... Show me: 335p, 450p, 216p...

◆ Give simple money problems for pupils to answer by mental calculation.

Show me double 95p. Show me half of £9. Total 45p and 95p.

◆ Ask pupils to show complements to £1, £5 and £10.

What must be added to these to make £1: 25p, 54p, 67p...?
What must be added to these to make £5: £3.50, £4.35, £1.85...?
What must be added to these to make £10: £8.75, £4.27, £6.05...?

Hundreds

Purpose	To work on calculations to 100 and calculations by 100. Pupils look at the properties of numbers to 100.
Development	Looking at hundredths, decimals and percentages.

Tell me about *Number facts for numbers to 100*

Pupils sit on chairs.

◆ Give a number and ask each pupil to give a different fact about it. Pupils take turns to answer with no exact repeats.

Start with 64. It is a square number, the product of 4 and 16, double 32, half 128...

Encourage use of odd, even, square, prime, multiple, total, difference...

Function machine *Division by 100, hundredths, decimals*

You will need: a set of fan numbers (page 43) for each pupil. Ask the pupils to place the decimal point on the top. Draw a simple function machine on the board.

◆ Choose the function ÷100 and write this on the machine. Tell pupils which numbers you are going to put into the machine. Play *Show me* to match which numbers come out.

Show me which number will come out if I put in: 8000, 9000, 12 000...
Show me which number will come out if I put in: 120, 370, 890...
Show me which number will come out if I put in: 46, 38, 67...
Show me which number will come out if I put in: 5, 9, 3...

The fans have only one of each digit so cannot show numbers such as 77.

A simple function machine

◆ Tell pupils which number is going to come out of the machine and ask them to show which number went in. Discuss multiplication undoing division and division undoing multiplication. Change the ÷100 to ×100 on the function machine and repeat the activity.

Shape totals *Totalling 3 numbers to 100 or 1*

Pupils work in co-operating pairs.
You will need: a set of fan numbers (page 43) for each pair.

◆ Draw a triangle on the board with 100 in the centre. Explain that there should be numbers at each corner of the triangle which should add up to the number in the middle. Write one corner number on the triangle. The pairs decide on two possible numbers for the other corners. Pupils show the answers. Discuss some alternatives. Repeat, using different corner numbers.

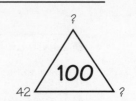

The corners must total 100

◆ Repeat the previous activity, writing 1 in the centre of the triangle and a hundredth number, either as a fraction or as a decimal, at one of the corners.

Decimal place value cards *Simple percentages*

You will need: a set of money cards for each pupil, made by adding the pounds sign (£) to a photocopy of the decimal place value cards (page 45).

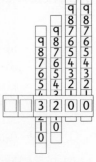

£2. 7 5

Money cards

◆ Ask pupils to use their money cards to show stated amounts.

Show me: £0.75, £3.25, £8.74...

Discuss finding hundredths of money and simple percentages.

Show me 1% of 1, 7, 10, 16...

Repeat for 10% and other simple percentages.

Number generator *Calculations with hundreds*

You will need: a number generator (page 42) for each pupil.

◆ Ask pupils to multiply multiples of 100 by small numbers.

Show me: 400 × 8, 900 × 7, 600 × 5, 1500 × 2...

◆ Repeat the activity, but find the products of hundreds numbers.

Show me: 300 × 400, 700 × 600, 900 × 600...

Similarly, multiply multiples of a hundred by tens and thousands.

What is 400 x 8?

Fan numbers *Rounding numbers*

You will need: a set of fan numbers (page 43) for each pupil.

◆ Ask pupils to round a range of numbers to the nearest 100 and show their answers.

Round these numbers to the nearest 100: 378, 921, 1377...

Rounding 378

◆ Ask pupils to round decimal numbers in the hundredths to the nearest whole, or tenth, and show their answers.

Round these numbers to the nearest tenth: 0.74, 0.85, 0.88...

Elastic band strips *Estimations of hundreds and hundredths*

You will need: a strip of card for each pupil to be marked off into ten equal sections. They slide an elastic band onto the strip, taut enough not to drop off.

◆ Tell pupils that one end of the marked strip is zero and the other is 1000. Ask them to move the band to show the positions of numbers such as 700 and 680. Ask pupils to show the position of other hundreds.

◆ Tell pupils that one end of the strip is zero and the other is 1. Ask them to move the elastic band to show the positions of hundredths such as: 0.72, 0.52, 0.29...

0   1

A strip marked off into ten divisions showing the approximate position of 0.52

Shapes

Purpose	To define the properties of a range of 2D and 3D shapes.
Development	Classifying 2D and 3D shapes using greater precision and a wider vocabulary. It is important to have a varied class set of polygons and polyhedra.

Behind the wall *Recognizing and naming 2D shapes*

Pupils work in co-operating groups.
You will need: a collection of 2D shapes for each group, a matching set for yourself and a simple free-standing wall, or screen, made from a cardboard box.

◆ Slowly slide up a polygon, behind a simple card wall and stop when part of it is showing.

Show me which shape you think this could be.

Pupils hold up the shapes which are possibilities. Discuss the alternatives.

Show a little more of the shape and repeat the *Show me* activity. Eventually make the whole shape visible. Check to see if the pupils know what the shape is called and its main properties. Talk about regular and irregular shapes.

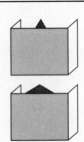

Two corners of the same quadrilateral. Which quadrilateral?

Repeat for different polygons, regular and irregular. Include tilted shapes so that pupils do not always associate shapes with one orientation.

Show me *Properties of 2D and 3D shapes*

Pupils work in co-operating groups.
You will need: sets of 2D and 3D shapes for each group.

◆ Give a clue to a mystery 2D shape. Each group discusses the clue and, when you ask them, they hold up the shape or shapes they think it might be. Discuss their choices and talk about alternatives.

My shape is a polygon with parallel sides.
My shape is a right angled quadrilateral which is not symmetrical.
My shape is a triangle with an angle greater than 90°.

You can adapt this activity by giving further clues about the mystery shapes until ambiguity has been removed. Between each new clue, allow time for sorting and response.

My shape is a quadrilateral. It is symmetrical. Two sides are parallel. It has no right angles. Only two sides are the same.

Pupils should know it must be a trapezium with two sides of the same length.

◆ Repeat the previous activity for 3D shapes. Discuss how prisms and pyramids can be defined by the shape of their base, or cross section.

My shape is a polyhedron with four faces.
My shape has all its faces identical, but they are not squares.
My shape has faces which are hexagons and rectangles.

Pass it on *Knowledge of 2D and 3D shape names and properties*

Pupils sit in a large circle facing inwards.
You will need: a collection of 2D and 3D shapes.

◆ This game is a little like *Pass the parcel*. Give the first pupil a shape. They state a fact about that shape before passing it on. The next person gives a different fact about the shape before passing it on. The activity should be co-operative, with the class trying to get the shape as far round the circle as possible. When they have exhausted the facts about a shape, replace it with a different one.

◆ Use 2D shapes to pass on. As well as naming the shape and the more obvious facts, prompt pupils to look for such properties as: right angles, symmetry, equal length of sides and angles, ability to tessellate. Widen vocabulary to include such descriptions as polygon, regular, irregular.

◆ Use 3D shapes to pass on. Prompt pupils to include descriptions of the shape and number of faces. Include the idea of symmetry, flat and curved faces, vertices and edges. Widen vocabulary to include prisms, pyramids, polyhedra.

Show me *Right angles and diagonals*

You will need: a collection of 2D shapes.

◆ Discuss angles in shapes. Play *Show me* activities such as:

Show me a shape which has: one right angle, no right angles, equal sides and right angles...

Discuss the shape angles which are more than or less than a right angle. Use the words 'acute' and 'obtuse'.

◆ Talk about diagonal lines in shapes and how they are the line from one corner to another, not always straight across the centre of the shape.

Show me a shape with equal diagonals. Show me a shape with five diagonals. Show me a shape with diagonals which meet at right angles.

I spy *Properties of 2D and 3D shapes*

Pupils work in co-operating groups.
You will need: a collection of 2D and 3D shapes, and a tray.

◆ Put out a tray of 3D shapes for all pupils to see. Ask one group to state a property of one of the shapes they can see on the tray. For example:

I spy a 3D shape.

The next group adds to this: *I spy a 3D shape with symmetry.*
Subsequent groups take turns to add to this. The aim is get as long a chain of properties as possible. For a hemisphere this could be:

I spy a 3D shape with symmetry, which does not tessellate, has no right angles, has no vertices, has one curved face, has one flat face, has a circle face...

◆ Repeat the previous activity for 2D shapes.

Angles and positions

| Purpose | To consider the dynamic aspects of angles by creating angles by turning. Pupils also cover the language of position. |

Angle strips *Turns and angles*

You will need: two Geostrips fastened together for each pupil. If you do not have Geostrips, use card strips fastened with brass split pins.

◆ Remind pupils what right angles are. Ask them to make and show a right angle with their strips. Ask pupils to make and show angles which are acute and obtuse.

Geostrips showing an angle less than a right angle

◆ Repeat the previous activity, except that degrees are used instead of right angles. Ask pupils to estimate 45°, 70°, 100°.

Angle maker *Angles and degrees*

You will need: an angle maker (page 47) for each pupil.

◆ Ask pupils to slot the circles together so that the sectors on the white circle are hidden – they are not needed for this activity. Ask them to slide the circles around to show a white sector which is: about a right angle, more than a right angle, an obtuse angle, about 45°, between 90° and 180°…

Showing an acute angle on an angle maker, sectors not showing

Showing 50° on an angle maker, 10° sectors showing

◆ Ask pupils to slot the circles together so that the sectors on the white circle are showing. Tell pupils that each sector is 10°. Ask them to slide the circles around to show a white sector which is 90°, 40°, 70°…

Show me *Positions and directions*

Pupils stand at least one arm's length from each other.

◆ With the aid of a compass, show the eight compass positions. Place signs on the wall if appropriate. Ask pupils to use their left or right arms to indicate the points, left, right, horizontal and vertical, clockwise and anticlockwise:

Put your left arm horizontally to the front. Point to south west with your right hand.

◆ Play *Simon says*. Pupils must do whatever Simon says, but if Simon does not say, then the pupils do not do it. For example:

Simon says 'Touch your right ear'. Pupils should do this action.
Simon says 'Point to north east with your left hand'. Pupils should do this.
Make half a turn clockwise. Pupils should not do this. Simon did not say so.

Time

| Purpose | To tell the time using 24 hour notation and with simple time calculations. |

Digital time maker *Telling the time on digital clocks*

You will need: a digital time maker (page 46) for each pupil.

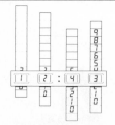

Digital time maker

◆ Talk about how time is written and how it is shown on video recorders and other timing devices. Ask pupils to show different times on their digital time makers.

Show me six twenty-three in the morning.
Show me three minutes past midnight.
Show me 3 o'clock in the afternoon.

Talk about a.m. and p.m. times and using 24 hour time.

◆ Ask pupils to make a stated time on their digital time maker. Then ask them to show: one hour later, 30 minutes later, 15 minutes earlier…

Digital time maker *Time calculations*

You will need: a digital time maker (page 46) for each pupil.

◆ Discuss rounding up to the next hour and how many minutes are needed. Ask pupils to show their responses to problems on the digital time makers.

Show me how many minutes to the next hour: 7.45, 4.35, 2.48…

Ask for the difference between two times, first within, then crossing, the hour.

How many minutes between: 4.10 and 4.55, 7.25 and 7.54, 6.02 and 6.50?
How many minutes between: 3.45 and 3.10, 8.50 and 8.20, 7.52 and 8.02?

◆ Give a time and ask pupils to show the time after a given period.

Show me 07.15. Now show me the time after 20 minutes.
Show me 15.25 Now show me the time after $1\frac{1}{2}$ hours.

Tell me about *Knowledge of time facts and vocabulary*

Pupils sit on chairs.

◆ Choose some time facts and question pupils about them. For example:

How many days in a leap year? How many days in a fortnight?
How many years in a decade? How many years in a millennium?
How many seconds in two minutes? How many minutes in four hours?

◆ Talk about minutes and seconds.

What can you do in one minute?
Eyes closed and put up your hand after you think a minute has passed.
How can we estimate how long a second is?

◆ Discuss special days and events from different cultures.

Number Cards

0	1	2	3
4	5	<u>6</u>	7
8	9	$\frac{1}{2}$	$\frac{1}{2}$
0	1	2	3
4	5	<u>6</u>	7
8	9		

Cut out these number cards.

INTERACTIVE MENTAL MATHS 5   © Peter Patilla 1999. Heinemann Educational Ltd. For copyright restrictions see reverse of title page

Place Value Grid

10 000 000	20 000 000	30 000 000	40 000 000	50 000 000	60 000 000	70 000 000	80 000 000	90 000 000
1 000 000	2 000 000	3 000 000	4 000 000	5 000 000	6 000 000	7 000 000	8 000 000	9 000 000
100 000	200 000	300 000	400 000	500 000	600 000	700 000	800 000	900 000
10 000	20 000	30 000	40 000	50 000	60 000	70 000	80 000	90 000
1000	2000	3000	4000	5000	6000	7000	8000	9000
100	200	300	400	500	600	700	800	900
10	20	30	40	50	60	70	80	90
1	2	3	4	5	6	7	8	9

Place counters on the grid to make numbers.

10 000 000	20 000 000	30 000 000	40 000 000	50 000 000	60 000 000	70 000 000	80 000 000	90 000 000
1 000 000	2 000 000	3 000 000	4 000 000	5 000 000	6 000 000	7 000 000	8 000 000	9 000 000
100 000	200 000	300 000	400 000	500 000	600 000	700 000	800 000	900 000
10 000	20 000	30 000	40 000	● 50 000	60 000	70 000	80 000	90 000
1000	2000	3000	4000	5000	6000	7000	8000	9000
100	200	● 300	400	500	600	700	800	900
10	20	30	40	50	● 60	70	80	90
1	2	3	4	5	6	7	8	9

The counters show the number 50 360.

© Peter Patilla 1999. Heinemann Educational Ltd. For copyright restrictions see reverse of title page

Number Generator

Cut slots along the **dotted** lines.

Cut out these strips to make a number generator.

9	9	9	9	9	9
8	8	8	8	8	8
7	7	7	7	7	7
6	6	6	6	6	6
5	5	5	5	5	5
4	4	4	4	4	4
3	3	3	3	3	3
2	2	2	2	2	2
1	1	1	1	1	1
0	0	0	0	0	0

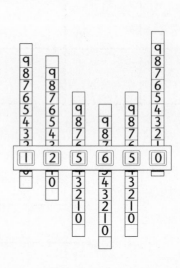

INTERACTIVE MENTAL MATHS 5   © Peter Patilla 1999. Heinemann Educational Ltd. For copyright restrictions see reverse of title page

Fan Numbers

Cut out these cards to make a number fan. Use a brass paper fastener.
Add the decimal point to make a decimal fan.

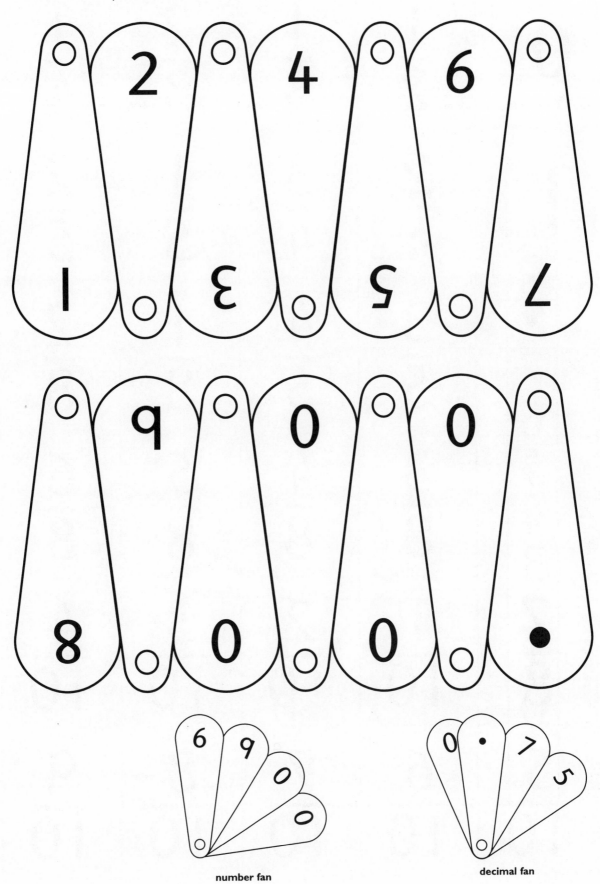

number fan

decimal fan

© Peter Patilla 1999. Heinemann Educational Ltd. For copyright restrictions see reverse of title page

INTERACTIVE MENTAL MATHS 5

Fraction Cards

Cut out these fraction cards.

0	$\dfrac{1}{2}$	$\dfrac{1}{3}$	$\dfrac{2}{3}$	$\dfrac{1}{4}$
1	$\dfrac{2}{4}$	$\dfrac{3}{4}$	$\dfrac{1}{5}$	$\dfrac{2}{5}$
	$\dfrac{3}{5}$	$\dfrac{4}{5}$	$\dfrac{1}{8}$	$\dfrac{2}{8}$
	$\dfrac{3}{8}$	$\dfrac{4}{8}$	$\dfrac{5}{8}$	$\dfrac{6}{8}$
$\dfrac{7}{8}$	$\dfrac{1}{10}$	$\dfrac{2}{10}$	$\dfrac{3}{10}$	$\dfrac{4}{10}$
$\dfrac{5}{10}$	$\dfrac{6}{10}$	$\dfrac{7}{10}$	$\dfrac{8}{10}$	$\dfrac{9}{10}$

INTERACTIVE MENTAL MATHS 5

© Peter Patilla 1999. Heinemann Educational Ltd. For copyright restrictions see reverse of title page

Decimal Place Value Cards

1.	0	0	1	0	1
2.	0	0	2	0	2
3.	0	0	3	0	3
4.	0	0	4	0	4
5.	0	0	5	0	5
6.	0	0	6	0	6
7.	0	0	7	0	7
8.	0	0	8	0	8
9.	0	0	9	0	9

0.0 0

 Cut out these decimal place value cards.

© Peter Patilla 1999. Heinemann Educational Ltd. For copyright restrictions see reverse of title page   INTERACTIVE MENTAL MATHS 5

Angle Maker/Protractor

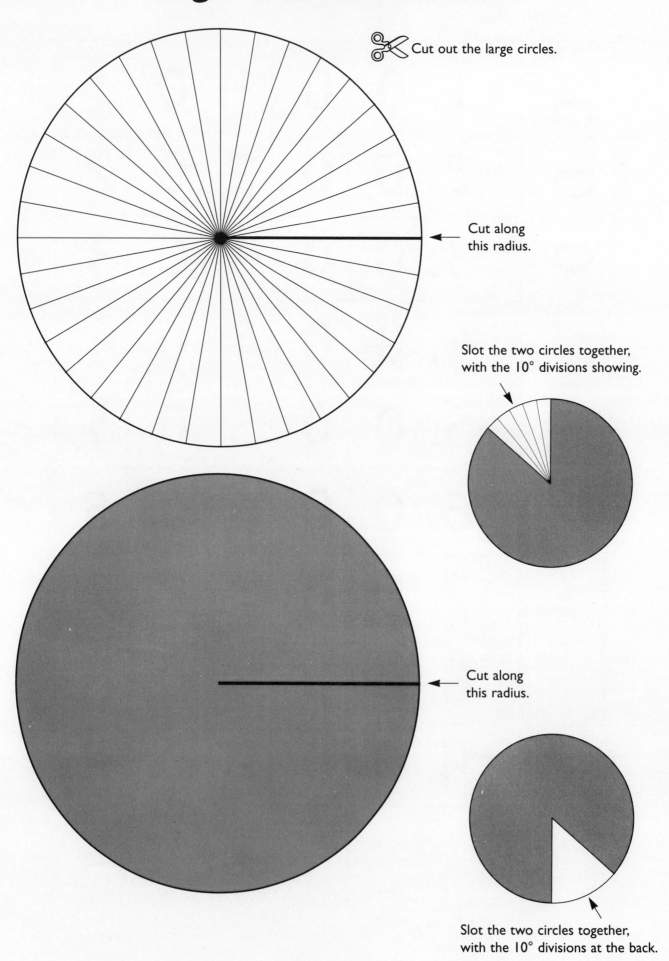

Cut out the large circles.

Cut along this radius.

Slot the two circles together, with the 10° divisions showing.

Cut along this radius.

Slot the two circles together, with the 10° divisions at the back.

INTERACTIVE MENTAL MATHS 5 © Peter Patilla 1999. Heinemann Educational Ltd. For copyright restrictions see reverse of title page

Digital Time Maker

		:		
....	....		....	....
....	....		....	....

✂ Cut slots along the **dotted** lines.

Cut out these strips to make a digital time maker.

	9		9
	8		8
	7		7
	6		6
	5	5	5
	4	4	4
	3	3	3
2	2	2	2
1	1	1	1
0	0	0	0

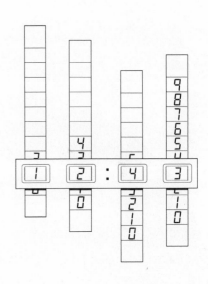

© Peter Patilla 1999. Heinemann Educational Ltd. For copyright restrictions see reverse of title page INTERACTIVE MENTAL MATHS 5